Top of the Mops

by Julia Donaldson

Illustrated by David Pattison

The Characters

The play is set in the hallway of the Millers' house.

ANDY MILLER,
a teenage rock musician.

CAROL MILLER,
Andy's mother,
an estate agent.

Scene One

Wednesday, early evening. Andy is sitting by the phone with a paper on his lap. He dials a number.

ANDY: Hello, I'd like to put an ad in your paper. Singer needed to join new band. Phone 483 5593. That's it. OK. Thank you. Goodbye.

CAROL: *(Coming out of the kitchen, sounding cross)* Andy, the freezer's been unplugged.

ANDY: What? Oh, sorry, Mum, I needed to plug my new amp in somewhere.

CAROL: What's wrong with your studio? Do you want me to turn it back into a spare room?

ANDY: No, of course not. The studio was just a bit ... crowded, that's all.

CAROL: In other words it was a complete tip, as usual.

ANDY: I'm sorry, Mum. I meant to plug the freezer back in.

CAROL: Well, it's too late now. You'll just have to have soggy beefburgers and melted ice-cream for supper.

ANDY: I've *said* I'm sorry.

CAROL: And *what's* this banana skin doing on the floor?

ANDY: I don't know – the Can-can, maybe.

CAROL: Ha ha, very funny.

ANDY: Keep your hair on, can't you Mum?

CAROL: How can I when I get back from work to find the house looking like this?

ANDY: Well, it's not all me. What about your bedroom?

CAROL: My bedroom is like Buckingham Palace compared with your studio. Now go and tidy it!

ANDY: I'll do it later.

CAROL: You'll do it now. Why are you always
           so lazy?

ANDY: *(Going out of the front door)* I must take
           after you.

(Carol throws the banana skin at him as he goes out.)

CAROL: He's right really. I can't stand housework
           either. What's this? *(Picking up the paper.)*
           "Evening News". Hmmmm. *(She dials a
           number.)* Hello, could I put an ad in, please?
           Cleaner wanted urgently. Phone 483 5593.
           Thank you. Goodbye.

Scene Two

Saturday morning. The phone rings. Andy comes out of the studio to answer it.

ANDY: Hi, Andy Miller here.

DOREEN: *(On the phone)* Hello, dear, my name's Doreen Blanket. I'm ringing about the job.

ANDY: Oh great! Um ... have you done this sort of thing before?

DOREEN: Oh yes, dear, I've worked for ever so many different people.

ANDY: That's good. Who have you been with, then?

DOREEN: Let's see ... The Browns, The Robinsons ...

ANDY: I haven't heard of them.

DOREEN: The Stones ...

ANDY: The Stones! Really? That's amazing! Er ... What sort of stuff do you like doing?

DOREEN: I'll do whatever needs doing – as long as it's not too heavy, that is.

ANDY: Oh no, we're not into heavy metal or anything.

DOREEN: That's good, because I've got a bad back. I can't do a lot of lifting. The last place I worked, they wanted me to lift these heavy metal dustbins.

ANDY: *(Puzzled)* Really? How strange.

DOREEN: Yes, they were a bit. Still, it takes all sorts, that's what I always say. That reminds me, there's something I ought to warn you about.

ANDY: What's that?

DOREEN: I do like to sing.

ANDY: Well, I should hope so!

DOREEN: You don't mind, then? That's good because the last people didn't like it at all.

ANDY: *(Suddenly a bit worried)* Oh dear. Well, I'd need to hear you of course. Could you come round today? At about two? It's 4 Vernon Gardens, by the way.

DOREEN: I'll be there!

ANDY: That's great! See you at two then, Doreen. Goodbye!

(Carol comes out of the kitchen.)

CAROL: Andy, you haven't cleared away the breakfast things.

ANDY: OK, OK. I'll do it.

(He goes into the kitchen. The phone rings. Carol answers it.)

CAROL: Hello, Carol Miller speaking.

SPIKE: *(On the phone)* Oh, hi, my name's Spike. I'm phoning about the job.

CAROL: How wonderful! Have you done this sort of work before, Spike?

SPIKE: Do you mean with a mike or without?

CAROL: With *Mike,* did you say? No, I don't think we need Mike as well. We're not that big, you know.

SPIKE: Who have you got, then?

CAROL: Just the one boy, Andy – mind you, that's quite enough!

SPIKE: Is he the drummer or what?

CAROL: How *did* you guess? Yes, he is. I'm afraid he's not very tidy – the studio is a terrible mess.

SPIKE: I don't mind that.

CAROL: Oh, you sound *wonderful,* Mike.

SPIKE: It's Spike.

CAROL: Spike, of course – Mike's the other one, isn't he?

SPIKE: By the way, I do quite a bit of writing.

CAROL: Good for you, Spike! I can tell you're a bright lad. Just don't carve your name on the furniture, will you? *(She laughs.)*

SPIKE: *(Sounding a bit confused)* No. Er … where do you live?

CAROL: We're at 4 Vernon Gardens. You couldn't come round today, Spike, could you? At about two?

SPIKE: Sure, I'll be there.

CAROL: That's terrific. Goodbye!

Scene Three

1.45 p.m., the same day. The doorbell rings and Carol answers it.

SPIKE: I'm sorry, I'm a bit early.

CAROL: That's fine, I'm just so *glad* you could come at all.

SPIKE: By the way, I forgot to ask what you call yourselves.

CAROL: I thought I told you – Miller.

SPIKE: Just "Miller"? Do you think that's catchy enough?

CAROL: Well, I'm not going to start changing my name – not even for you, Spike!

SPIKE: No, OK. Er ... where's the studio then?

CAROL: The studio? Are you sure you want to start there? It's in a terrible state, I'm afraid.

SPIKE: I don't mind.

CAROL: Oh you *wonderful* young man! It's that door there. And all the stuff you'll need is in this cupboard. Well, I'll just pop out to the shops if that's all right?

SPIKE: What, *now*?

CAROL: I won't be long.

SPIKE: OK, then.

(Carol goes out. Spike opens the broom cupboard.)

SPIKE: I can't see any mikes or amps in here. Maybe they're behind all this cleaning stuff. *(He takes out the hoover, brooms, mop, etc.)* Oh well, I'll have a look in the studio. *(He goes into the studio.)*

Scene Four

Andy comes in through the front door.

ANDY: Amazing! Mum's got the hoover out
for once.

(The doorbell rings and Andy answers it.)

ANDY: Oh hi, are you Doreen?

DOREEN: That's right, dear. I see you're all ready for
me! Oh, that's a very nice hoover you've
got there, it's the latest model, isn't it?

ANDY: I don't know.

DOREEN: Where shall I plug it in?

ANDY: Hey, you don't need to do that. I thought you were going to sing!

DOREEN: Oh, you are a one! I do like a bit of music while I work, I must admit.

ANDY: Do you know any blues numbers?

DOREEN: No, dear, nothing like that. It's the shows I like. "The Sound of Music", that's got some lovely songs in it, hasn't it?

ANDY: Well, it's not really my scene.

DOREEN:	Then there's "Oliver", of course. "Where is Love?" – that's my favourite.
ANDY:	Do you like "Cats"?
DOREEN:	Not really, dear, they shed their hair all over the furniture, you see.
ANDY:	*(Sounding doubtful)* Yes, well, why don't we go into the studio anyway? Maybe we could try out some indy stuff.

(From the studio comes the faint sound of a guitar being strummed.)

DOREEN:	It sounds like there's someone in there already.
ANDY:	Probably my mum. She's always nosing around.
SPIKE:	*(Singing softly in the studio)* Woke up this morning. Never felt so bad ...
DOREEN:	She's got a very low voice, hasn't she?
ANDY:	That's not Mum. *(He looks through the keyhole, then whispers.)* It's a bloke! It must be a burglar!

DOREEN: *(Whispering)* You don't say! Shall we go in and tackle him?

ANDY: No, he could be dangerous. Look, I'll watch the door while you phone the police.

DOREEN: Here – have a broom. *(She hands him a broom, then dials 999.)* Police, please. Hello, we've got a burglar.

Scene Five

Carol returns with the shopping. She sees Andy with the broom.

CAROL: *(In a loud voice)* Andy, what are you doing?

ANDY: Shhhhh!

DOREEN: *(On the phone)* What was that? Where am I calling from? 4 Vernon Gardens.

CAROL: And what's this woman doing using our phone?

ANDY: Mum, there's a burglar in the studio!

(The door of the studio opens and out comes Spike, carrying drumsticks. Andy pounces on him and grabs him.)

ANDY: Not so fast! Those are my drumsticks!

CAROL: Don't be silly – it's not a burglar, it's the cleaner.

DOREEN: *(Dropping the phone in surprise)* No it's not, it's my Spike!

SPIKE: *(To Doreen)* Mum! What are you doing here?

CAROL:	Really, Spike, fancy asking your mum round to use the phone the second my back's turned.
SPIKE:	I didn't ask her – I don't know what she's doing here.
CAROL:	A likely story! And look – you've just left all the cleaning things lying in a heap!
DOREEN:	Really, Spike, what do you mean by coming and messing up these nice people's house?
CAROL:	He's supposed to be cleaning it.
DOREEN:	*(To Andy)* Well, I like that! You could have told me you'd found somebody else to do the cleaning.
SPIKE:	I'm not supposed to be cleaning. I'm supposed to be singing!
DOREEN:	Well, that makes more sense, I must say. He's got a lovely voice, my Spike. Well, it runs in the family.
ANDY:	*(Letting go of Spike)* Do you like blues?
SPIKE:	Sure.
CAROL:	What's going on? I don't understand.

DOREEN: I think I'm beginning to. Let's go back a bit
          – who put the ad in the paper?

CAROL: I did.

ANDY: No, I did.

DOREEN: So there were *two* ads – one for a cleaner and one for a singer. My son Spike here wanted the singing job but you thought he was the cleaner. Am I making sense, dear?

CAROL: Yes, go on!

DOREEN: Well, then, I came round to do the cleaning, only your Andy tried to get me singing in his studio.

ANDY:	Only Spike was there already. We thought he was a burglar.
DOREEN:	And we phoned the police – what a hoot!
CAROL:	I think I get it. There's just one thing that's puzzling me, though.
DOREEN:	What's that, dear?
CAROL:	Your face – I feel sure I've seen you before somewhere.

DOREEN: I seem to recognize you too. It's going back a bit, though.

CAROL: Wasn't it just before I had Andy?

DOREEN: And I was expecting Spike.

CAROL: That's it!

DOREEN: The hospital baby classes!

CAROL: Do you remember that rubber doll we had to bath?

DOREEN: Weren't you the one who kept on dropping her?

CAROL: Yes! And you were the one who was always singing!

DOREEN: And do you remember the party after the babies were born?

CAROL: Yes, of course! Andy was so *red* – well, purple, really, like a little wrinkled plum! So sweet!

ANDY: Mum, shut up!

DOREEN: And poor old Spike had that dreadful nappy rash.

SPIKE: Stop it, Mum!

CAROL: And then Andy was sick all over that woman with the twins.

ANDY: *Mum!*

SPIKE: They're away, we'll never stop them now.

ANDY: Do you want to come into the studio and try out some soul numbers?

SPIKE: Good idea.

(They go into the studio.)

CAROL: You were wonderful – you mopped up all the sick.

DOREEN: Mrs Mop, that's me! Now, dear, I'm just itching to get my hands on your beautiful hoover.

CAROL: You're still wonderful!

DOREEN: You don't mind if I sing, do you?

CAROL: Not at all. You couldn't clean the cooker as
            well, could you? It's filthy, I'm afraid.

ANDY: (Coming out of the studio with Spike) Hey,
            Mum, there's a police car outside the
            house.

(They all go to the hall window and look out.)

CAROL: So there is – and two policemen are getting out of it.

DOREEN: And a sniffer dog as well – isn't he lovely?

CAROL: I wonder where they're going?

ANDY: Look, they're coming up the front steps.

EVERYONE: Oh no!

(There is a loud ring at the bell.)

Peck, P Peck
Peck

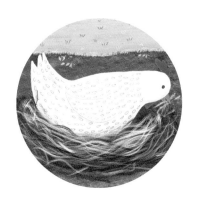

Kasia Reay

Illustrated by Selina Rayner

Schofield & Sims

Meg can sit and pe<u>ck</u>.

Meg can sit and nap.

Meg can sit and pe<u>ck</u>.

Meg can get up and p<u>e</u>c<u>k</u>.

Peg can tap and tap.

Peg can tap and pop up!

Peg can run to Meg the mum.